GUS THE FOX
SCRAP BOOK

foreword by noel fielding

A FOREWORD BY NOEL FIELDING

I remember the first time I met Gus the Fox I was standing on his head and suddenly, completely out of nowhere he reached into his pocket, pulled out a rusty knife and sliced open my nut sack. Hundreds and Thousands poured out all over the grass and I was rushed to hospital. Five minutes after we arrived Gus had sex with an Indian doctor in the bins where they keep used bandages. What a character.

The great thing about Gus is he'll go to extraordinary lengths just to have a giggle. One time he convinced a surgeon friend of his to swap our heads. When the anaesthetic wore off I spent the week scaring turkeys on an organic range with the Canadian band Rush. Gus went completely mental and ended up on Record Breakers giving himself a blow job in front of Roy Castle.

As soon as I start thinking about Gus the memories come flooding back. One time we broke into Paperchase, flooded the place, and re-filmed the Life of Pi using an ashtray and a dead kitten.

I can also recall with great fondness the time Gus gnawed a perfectly formed hole in the shape of number seven through one of my ankles while I was asleep. He dragged me to an alley and shone coloured lights through the hole onto a series of dustbin lids, charging some posh people £15 to watch. We were immediately nominated for the Turner Prize. We were favourites to win until Gus urinated onto Nicholas Serota's oyster card, then tried to pass off his actions as a statement in support of the rights for bears to have sex with Sean Penn.

At this point Nicholas punched Gus in the face wearing a solid gold mitten. Gus's skull crumbled into a fine white powder and for a week his head resembled a woman's purse, soft and folding in on itself. I managed to give it back some shape using a wire coat hanger as the framework and padding it out with pieces of ripped up dungarees from a clown we had accidentally murdered the night before.

He once told me he was allergic to sitcoms and ham and I'll never forget the day we visited Watney's pond and convinced 150,000 tadpoles that they all had **SARS**. We laugh about that now but at the time it was hysterical.

When Gus told me he was planning to write this book I immediately stuffed him into an old rollerskate, forced some felt tips into his eye sockets and pushed him down Primrose Hill into a barrage of heavy traffic. The last image I have of Gus is of him being dragged towards Camden under a black cab, sparks flying everywhere. I remember feeling a strange mixture of sad and horny.

I love Gus like a brother, even though he gave me a yeast infection. He is one of the truly great foxes. He's a top bloke, a good mate and an utter penis. He's a one off, and in a world of reality TV and celebrity bullshit we need Gus more than ever. Enjoy his book (I reckon it will be shit) but the mere fact that a fox has managed to get a book published is enough reason to karate chop him in the face when you see him next. Cheers Gus, (don't ever contact me again). Noel. X

MY NAME'S GUS
AN INTRODUCTION

So you've decided to buy/steal a scrapbook written by a fox. Congratulations. I'd be fascinated to find out why, I really would. Perhaps you've read everything else in the world. Perhaps you've read absolutely everything by Tolstoy, Dostoyevski, Dickens and Franz Kafka and you've been forced to work your way down the literary ladder until you've been left with no other options. Nothing else left to read apart from a scrapbook written by a fox. If that's the case then I'll apologise in advance. The book contains some pretty salacious stuff about what animals and celebrities get up to when you lot aren't looking, but it's hardly going to be nominated for a Pulitzer Prize any time soon. So why did I bother?

Well I grew up in Tunbridge Wells, Kent. I had a pretty rough upbringing. My mum ate most of my brothers and sisters when I was young, so it wasn't exactly a very happy home life. When I was about three my father was shot in the face by a man with a little trumpet and he got turned into a posh hat. It was one bloody thing after another. I used to try and keep out of everyone's way when I was young. I'd spend hours and hours sitting in the shed talking to the wasps and writing poems about my favourite episodes of Dad's Army.

A couple of years later I murdered my own Gran in a fight over some sausages and everyone thought it would be best if I fucked off to live in London.

Everyone I met was a prick so I spent a lot of time in my filthy lodgings compiling a scrapbook of all my thoughts and findings. I suppose you could describe me as some kind of urban zoologist who's compiled a unique and seminal dossier of such cultural importance that it makes Charles Darwin's efforts look like the scribblings of a div kid. I suppose you could also describe me as a sort of gonzo journalist reporting from the frontline on the city's dark and seedy underbelly. Skulking surreptitiously beneath London's tacky, superficial veneer whilst disclosing previously unknown information about the society of creatures you will often only ever catch a fleeting glimpse of as they slink off into the gloaming. You could describe me like that but it would make you sound like a bit of a cunt.

My name's Gus. I'm a fox. This is my scrapbook full of shit.

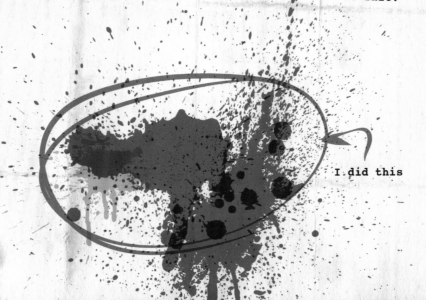

I did this

A DESCRIPTION OF CWIS PACKHAM'S BUNGALOW

It's in an area behind the industrial estate (between Homebase and Carpetright). You wouldn't really expect there to be a bungalow there because the whole area isn't really residential and there are so many nettles. The front porch area is littered with broken glass and crisp packets (mainly Wotsits). The whole porch bit is sort of covered in a layer of grease or petrol or something and the whole place emits a sense of gloom. The front door is green and obscured by a black gate. It's the type of thing you might find in like, say, a prison or psychiatric unit.

In the hallway there's a big pile of gas cylinders (presumably awaiting to be fly-tipped in the woods). On the wall there's a framed picture of a bear sitting in a rowing boat. It's been done in crayons but it's actually quite good and you can tell it's been done by someone who knows their way around a pencil case. The walls in the hallway are a sort of black colour - almost as though they're covered in soot. The carpet is quite old and reminds me of the sort of thing you might find in a pub in the 1970s.

Straight ahead and there's a small kitchen. There are lots of bin bags on the floor and they sort of buzz and vibrate due to the fact that they're full of flies. Cwis often says that he half expects them to "simply fly out of the bungalow under their own volition."

The kitchen panels are a kind of mint green colour and are covered in Panini football stickers of all of Cwis's favourite players. There is a strip light on the ceiling which flickers and buzzes, almost in rhythm to the flies in the bin bags from earlier. The window looks out into a field of nettles and is covered in snowflakes which you can sort of tell were sprayed on there about six or seven years ago.

Moving through to the living room now and it's quite small, even for one man living alone. It has Thomas the Tank Engine wallpaper which suggests that at some point it may have been a child's bedroom. There's a bookshelf running along one of the walls which features several books and VHS cassettes about birds and animals but, for the most part it's just full of porn.

In the middle of the room there's an elaborate dining table (the legs are carved to look like mermaids). In the corner of the room is a chair and a small portable television. On the wall - above the mantlepiece bit - there's another crayon drawing (probably by the same artist as before). It's a picture of Cwis with Terry Nutkins and Michaela Strachan on the set of The Really Wild Show. On the wall opposite someone has graffitied the word 'EGGNOG' in large purple letters. There are no windows or lights in this room.

Finally, a quick comment about the bedroom which, when all is said and done, isn't dissimilar to a bird's nest. The bed has been expertly crafted from scraps of linen and by all accounts is very comfortable. The walls are covered in newspaper clippings and photographs of friends and loved ones. On the shelf there is a pot plant (dead), a hairdryer, a framed photograph of Morrissey and a gun.

FOX SLANG

RIZZLEKICKS (noun) /Riz-Al-Kix/ -
This is slang for the convulsive fit that a fox or other wild animal can go into if it consumes petrol. Sometimes this act can be enjoyed recreationally. i.e : Vile Clive drank fuck loads of Castrol GTX out of a tramp's shoe and got the rizzlekicks so bad that he almost died.

BRUSH-STROKER (noun) /Brush-Stroke-Er/ -
This is what we call people who bum foxes. i.e : Yeah, my mate Unbelievable Stephen reckons that Jonathan Dimbleby is a bit of a brush-stroker. Going to steer well clear of that bugger's garden from now on thank you very much.

STINGLING (verb) /Sting-gling/ -
The act of getting off with a wasp (behind a leisure centre). i.e : I've been stingling a wasp I met by the bins. Think I'm going to marry the cunt. His name's David Jason. Like the actor who played Frost and Del Boy.

BAD-SALAD (noun) /Bad-Salad/ -
A meal prepared in a prostitute's wig. i.e I had a bad-salad for my tea. It mainly tasted like jizz.

COCKADOODLING (verb) /Cock-A-Dood-Ling/ -

The act of punching a hen so hard in the throat that the little red bit on top its head blows up and it lays a red egg.
i.e : I've just been cockadoodling. Why else do you think I'm eating this red egg?

INCYGNIFICANT (adjective) /In-Sig-Nif-Ik-Ant/ -

Any animal smaller than a swan. (Any animal that you shouldn't have too much trouble bullying). i.e : When I realised that the dog was incygnificant, I kicked it in the bollocks and called it a prick.

MONGTH (verb) /Mong-Th/ -

A moth that has cerebral palsy.
i.e : I got trapped in a shed with a mongth the other day. That was a laugh. Not.

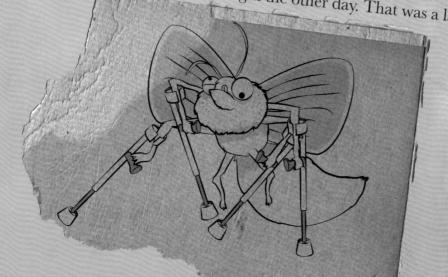

A TYPICAL DAY

1 - Wake up.

2 - Yawn and have a little think about the day ahead.

3 - Vomit up yesterday's dinner (bugs / slop / filth etc) in corner of revolting pit.

4 - Have a little look at bollocks (Oh dear. They're not looking in very good nick today are they? At least they haven't fucking fallen off yet.)

5 - Breakfast.

6 - Wander up canal taking some time out to bark at swans and people in wheelchairs.

7 - Meet Sexy Chris (Why is Sexy Chris dressed up as Jesus? Sexy Chris is such a knob.)

8 - Continue wandering about. (Have a mince through the graveyard for instance.)

9 - Visit Clunes.

10 - Rummage through bins / make a right pig's ear of some cunt's driveway.

11 - Visit prostitutes for snacks and cuddles.

12 - Return to lodgings.

13 - Have an unpleasant and painful shit at mouth of cave.

14 - Curl up and fall asleep (whilst mumbling about wasps).

* Make sure to constantly scream and yell like an idiot, for no reason, between points 6 and 10

COLIN HONG

緩衝材
内袋：PE
保護シート：

®

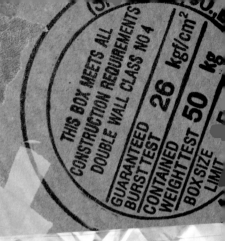
COCK

Colin is a wood pigeon. He thinks he was born in China but he wasn't.

He was born in an egg. In Clapton.

He once got bummed by a gypsy in a tunnel.

He's got gout in one of his legs.

He sometimes wears a hat.

He's not really one of my mates to be honest.

He's a fucking cock.

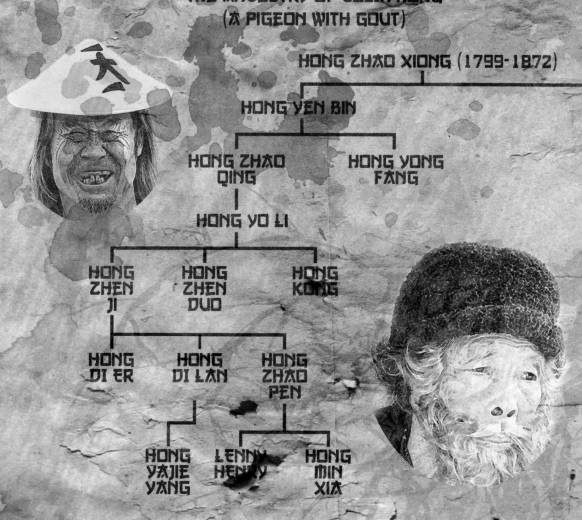

HONG FAMILY TREE
THE ANCESTRY OF COLIN HONG
(A PIGEON WITH GOUT)

HONG ZHAO XIONG (1799-1872)

HONG YEN BIN

HONG ZHAO QING — HONG YONG FANG

HONG YO LI

HONG ZHEN JI — HONG ZHEN DUO — HONG KONG

HONG DI ER — HONG DI LAN — HONG ZHAO PEN

HONG YAJIE YANG — LENNY HENRY — HONG MIN XIA

科林香港是一個陰戶

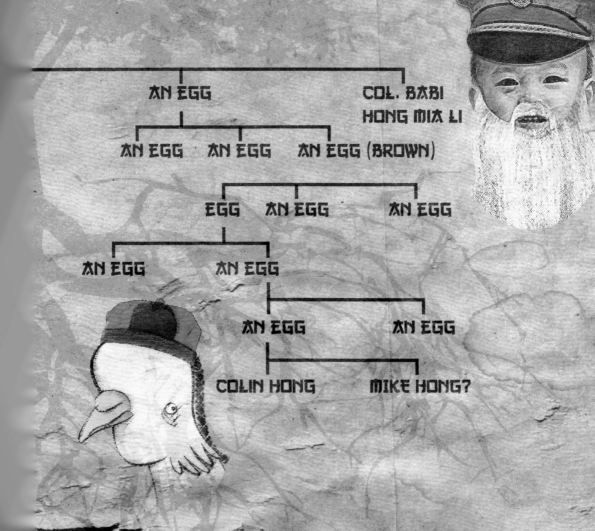

(extract from) MY DIARY

MONDAY

I woke up and it was raining.

I spent most of the morning watching a toad trying to climb out of a bath. He couldn't do it. He got nowhere fucking close and died at around lunchtime.

At lunchtime Cwis Packham rugby tackled me to the ground and put a tampon in my ear which put me in a bad mood for the rest of the day.

In the evening I went for a wander and saw a hen wearing brogues. It's one of the funniest things I've ever seen. He looked like such a cunt. Mainly because he was a hen. Spent the rest of the night rubbing Castrol GTX into a cygnet.

TUESDAY

I woke up and went for a walk down the canal. Whilst I was out a starling told me that my penis looks like "a tiny acorn that's been chewed on by a poorly dog". Great. Nice start to the day.

I spent the rest of the morning sneaking up behind a hedgehog and shouting the word clitoris into his ear. After about four hours he got really angry and started crying. Bumped into my mate Ryan Bannister who told me that he'd just got married to a slug. What a dickhead.

At about 4pm Eamonn Holmes strapped roller skates onto all my feet and sat about laughing whilst I fell over, crashing into everything and cursing the fat cunt under my breath. I had dinner with my friend Mick Hull but we fell out because he started insisting that he'd fucked Beyonce when she was still in Destiny's Child. I knew he was talking all kinds of shit because Mick's a daddy long legs and he lives in a lawnmower.

WEDNESDAY

Got up late.

Went to the City Farm to see what was going on. Bill Oddie was trying to teach the pigs how to speak English. He was getting very frustrated and calling them all a bunch of "stupid bastards". At one point he started shooting his service revolver into the sky and weeping. It was extraordinary.

At 11am I squeezed a bat into a carton of Um Bongo and lobbed it in the canal.

After I had my lunch I did a wee on a fuse box and a building caught fire. Everyone was running about screaming and shouting. (One man started crying and threw his shoes at me.)

As I was wandering home I bumped into a mouse called Lawrence Shoe. It's fucking crazy how racist mice are. We started talking about Jews and he got so angry that his eyes started bleeding.

I found an egg on my way home. A goose climbed out of it (hatched) called me a poof and strolled off up the canal. What a total arsehole.

Spent the rest of the evening in a foul mood.

THURSDAY

Woke up and got bummed by a gang of bin men.

Spent the rest of the morning making doves cry. Prince was spot on. It's a right laugh.

At midday I met a deaf fox called Lewis Chunk, he kept trying to howl. It was brilliant. He hadn't got the hang of it at all.

Early afternoon I punched a jackdaw in the throat because he kept saying "eggs are the new legs" which doesn't make any fucking sense at all. It really annoyed me.

Later on I had a little sleep. When I woke up someone had stapled a little hat onto my head that had the word 'faggot' written on it. When I looked around I could see Jeremy Paxman sat on a park bench sniggering to himself. The jokes on him though because it fell off after about eight hours.

At about 8pm I got in an argument with my mate Delicate Paul because he kept insisting that all foxes are blind. I kept trying to reason that neither of us are blind for a kick off but he wasn't having any of it.

I went out for a wander at night and met a bat called Callum Brine. He said that he didn't need eyes and that "eyes are for cunts". Then he flew off, straight into the side of a bus shelter.

FRIDAY

Last night I had a dream about a frog with fucking massive sideburns and woke up with an erection.

When I went out I met a Spoon-Billed Sandpiper who spent ages and ages moaning about the fact that he can't get a job because he looks like a cunt with a spoon strapped to his face. I killed him, fucked him and ate him.

Accidentally pissed in my own face.

At midday I walked into an old lady's flat on my hind legs and did a little dance on her coffee table. She fell to her knees and started weeping so I left.

In the afternoon I decided to paint a swan. I used a Pearl/Satin finish emulsion and he sank to the bottom of the canal and died.

I spent all night yelling at a shed.

SATURDAY

Woke up and glued a load of ants onto my face. Can't for the life of me remember why.
Feeling a bit all over the place today.

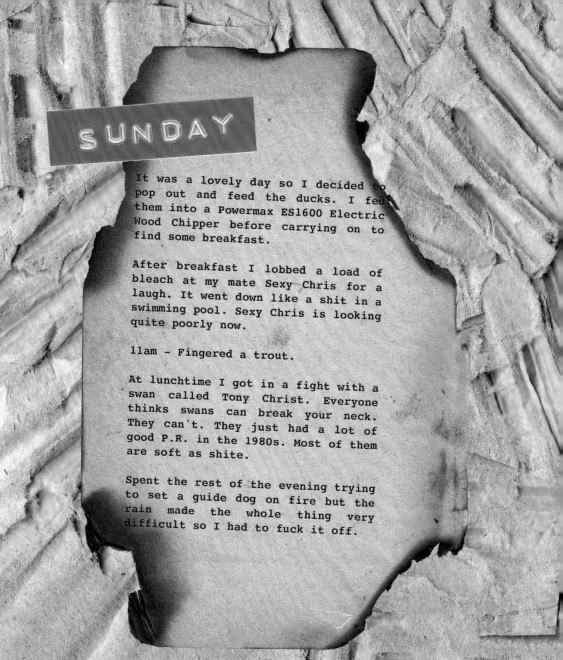

SUNDAY

It was a lovely day so I decided to pop out and feed the ducks. I fed them into a Powermax ES1600 Electric Wood Chipper before carrying on to find some breakfast.

After breakfast I lobbed a load of bleach at my mate Sexy Chris for a laugh. It went down like a shit in a swimming pool. Sexy Chris is looking quite poorly now.

11am - Fingered a trout.

At lunchtime I got in a fight with a swan called Tony Christ. Everyone thinks swans can break your neck. They can't. They just had a lot of good P.R. in the 1980s. Most of them are soft as shite.

Spent the rest of the evening trying to set a guide dog on fire but the rain made the whole thing very difficult so I had to fuck it off.

NEW YEAR'S RESOLUTIONS

1 - Stop growling at motorbikes. It's a waste of time.

2 - Clean some of the corpses out of the corner of the old pit. The smell keeps making guests vomit all over the lovely crockery.

3 - Spend a little bit less time staring at testicles and weeping. I know they're in a right old state and look like a sandblasted tomato but there's not much that can be done about that now. Time to pick yourself up and move on. Get a new hobby / go for a little jog. Anything to take your mind off those wretched bollocks.

4 - See a bit less of Martin Clunes.

5 - Stop getting married to moths. (This shouldn't be that difficult. Concentrate. You can do this.)

6 - Start being a bit more honest with people. If Sexy Chris turns up wearing leather trousers again then don't just smile politely, tell him he looks like a fucking cunt. Urge him to take his own life.

7 - Break it off with Emma Watson. There's no sexual chemistry and you both know it.

8 - Murder more hens.

9 - Eat more/some fruit.

10 - Stop moonwalking every time you see Bunty Hoven. She's not impressed and last time you did it you fell off the shed roof and she thought you were a fucking bell end.

an Extract from my Erotic Novel

: NOT REALLY GOT A TITLE YET. IT'LL PROBABLY BE SOMETHING QUITE ABSTRACT AND, SORT OF, POETIC. IT SHOULD BE SOMETHING THAT MAKES YOU PICTURE A MINGE IN YOUR MIND'S EYE (OR EVEN A GREAT BIG COCK AND BALLS).

I WANT THE FRONT COVER TO BE OF ME, SAT IN A SHED, STIFF AS A POST AND LOOKING OUT OF THE WINDOW AT A MAN IN DUNGAREES BUMMING A HERON UP AGAINST A TREE OR SOMETHING.

(I'D ALSO LIKE THE FRONT COVER TO BE DONE IN COLOURING PENCILS BY SOMEONE WHO, THOUGH NOT SHIT AT ART, WOULDN'T GET, SAY, MUCH MORE THAN A GRADE 'C' IN THEIR A -LEVEL ART EXAM.)

CHAPTER 1

'...She looked at me vacantly from behind the bins. Under the dull, flickering glare of the street lights she silently licked some leftover yoghurt out an old Crunch Corner that was covered in bees. She looked distant, as though a piece of her had been lost. Occasionally when the headlights of a passing car rolled past and illuminated her face, she would look over at me knowingly. She could tell I was staring at her but she didn't seem to mind. She craved the attention. This was the first time I'd ever met Brenda Stout, and, even though we were in a dank alley behind a fishmongers in Dalston, she was, without doubt, the most beautiful fox I'd ever seen. If I'd have known that three days later I'd be banging her from behind with my pork sword until her arsehole looked like a sandblasted tomato then I think I'd have fallen down with joy and wept right there and then. For now however, it was time to turn on the charm. I walked over to her all smooth 'n' that and told her a funny story about my penis. She cackled so hard that she farted, startling a cat and making it fall off a Ford Mondeo...'

(I CAN'T HELP WORRYING ABOUT THIS BLOODY TITLE. I KEEP THINKING THAT THERE'S GOT TO BE SOMETHING IN THE FACT THAT CUNNING AND CUNNILINGUS SOUND SO SIMILAR ... SOMETHING LIKE 'CUNNILINGUS AS A FOX' OR SOMETHING MAYBE. BUT THEN I'M THINKING THAT 'FOX' RHYMES WITH 'COCKS' AS WELL AND I'D QUITE LIKE TO, SORT OF, GET THAT IN THERE AS WELL.)

Pigeons

Talk about thick, these guys barely know what day of the week it is. If you've ever tried to have a chat with one then you'll know what I'm talking about. I once met a pigeon who'd spent about £4,000 on trainers. He can't even bloody wear them. I try and avoid them most of time because, despite the fact you can't have a half decent conversation with a pigeon, they're not really worth eating. Because you lot are such a nasty bunch of cunts, you put acid on the roofs of all the buildings in central London and because pigeons are so fucking stupid, they keep traipsing through it, again and again. That's why pigeons have feet that look (but don't taste) like popcorn. Anyway, my mate Donald Chocolate ate a pigeon once and it still had all this acid shit all over it's feet and it burnt old Don's mouth and lips. Now he looks a bit like Pete Burns and everyone gives him a hard time and calls him a prick. So I don't bother eating them unless I'm bloody starving.

Owls

People seem to have this idea that owls are 'wise', but I once sold an owl a tampon for £40. £40 for one tampon. Owls can be alright though. My mate Sexy Chris is an owl. He can be a bit of a pleb. Like all owls he believes his own hype. He thinks he's pretty intelligent and sophisticated but he's just a twat really. Once I caught him trying to eat his dinner with cutlery. He looked like such an idiot — he could barely hold the fork. The other day we got hammered on M-Cat and I convinced him to pluck all his feathers out for a laugh. He did and it was brilliant because he looked nude. Now he can't fly though and he hasn't eaten for a while. We're all quite worried that he might die.

Coots

Coots are racists. They are extremely unpleasant birds and once a coot (Troy Winters) made me so I angry that I punched him until both me and Troy were crying. It's weird that they're so different to moorhens who are actually a bloody good laugh.

Moles

They live in soil, you hardly ever see them and they have a right attitude problem. The other day a mole popped up, blinked at me, called me a wanker and fucked off back underground. I can do without that sort of thing to be honest. I did meet a nice mole once. His name was Tom Shoe. We had a bit of a laugh. He was always wearing this tiny little bomber jacket though, so even he was a bit of a plum to be fair.

Eels

I once saw an eel commit suicide. He jumped out of the canal and into the spokes of someone's fixie bike. Me and my mate Double Denim David laughed so much that we got nose bleeds and Dave fell in the canal and went over a weir. I've never had a chat with an eel. Apparently they're quite depressing characters. Very neurotic and negative. This is what I've heard from the swans and the ducks. My mate Violent Clive uses an eel as a sort of belt/scarf. He looks like an enormous bell end.

Rats

There's fucking loads of them and they taste delicious. Apparently there are about 7,500,000 rats in London. Even my mate Bollocks Steve couldn't eat that many in one sitting and he's a right chunky bastard. Rats basically wander about in gangs, effing and jeffing and thinking they're the dog's bollocks, until you get one on his own and then it's all 'Sorry mate I was joking' and 'Please don't hit me mate, my mum's got cancer'. They're spineless and I simply cannot get along with them. Having said that they are delicious. I don't know if it's all the crap they eat or the fact they knock about in bins and sewers but once you've had rat there's no going back. I once found a rat in the canal. It was all bald and bloated — it was one of the best days of my life.

Grey Squirrels

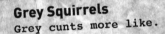

Grey cunts more like.

THIS YEAR'S christmas WISH LIST

1 - A bald rat

2 - Wasps

3 - A top hat/condoms

4 - A swan grinder

5 - A Terry's Chocolate Orange

6 - Some sort of ham (preferably rancid/old)

7 - A puffin (possibly wearing a little bomber jacket if possible)

8 - Bunty Hoven

9 - A brand new pair of testicles

10 - 1000 HENS

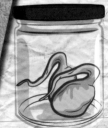

VILE CLIVE

Clive is a fox. He's quite fat. He's got the word 'Whore' written on his forehead from the time a talented tramp carved it on there with a butterfly knife. Once when he was sitting in the park a mole crawled up through the soil and went straight up his arse. He was running about panicking and I laughed so much that I was sick all over Sexy Chris.

K471C A0

VILE CLIVE'S ESTATE AGENTS

39G DOWNERS ROAD, DALSTON
£880pcm

Breathtaking apartment with hardly any damp/smears.
Just minutes away from nearest pavement.
Comes with free radiators and light bulbs (neither in working condition).

23 'THE CABIN', IN THE WOODS, BEHIND HOMEBASE
£1100pcm

Sophisticated bachelor pad in the middle
of the woods with stunning view of
electricity pylon.
Fully furnished with various metal tables
and trays of surgical equipment.
Ideal for first time killer/rapist.

'THE NEST', REGENTS CANAL, ISLINGTON
$80, 900

Grade 2 listed nest for sale. Great first time buy for a family of swans/humans. This unique 'thatched' property has been built from sticks, weeds, packets of Wotsits, Johnny bags and various other shit. Steeped in history, this nest was once part of a murder investigation after police found a kettle containing six human penises in it in 2004. Always going to be an interesting talking point over the dinner table. (Dinner table not included/recommended.)

ROYAL HOUSE, HOUNDS COURT, LAMBETH
£890pcm

Flat share opportunity for open-minded tenant in this charming, detached and extremely characterful property.
You'll never be lonely again sharing a room with 12 bin men and their dogs. No smokers.

'THE BUCKETS', HAMPSTEAD HEATH,
£430pcm

Beat the recession with this exciting and portable housing option. Pop the bucket on your head, lean against a tree and you'll be magically whisked away to spend the night in the house of your dreams (best used in conjunction with heroin). This charming property really is as good as your own imagination. AN ABSOLUTE BARGAIN!
(A good coat is recommended if you don't wish

to be killed by the winter frosts.)

RECIPE #1
WALTHAM POCKET

1 - Cover your hands in batter and turn on the oven.

2 - Boil all the eggs. ALL THE EGGS!

3 - Punch a swan in the throat, relax, for God's sake! It's your party! Let your hair down and have some fun for once!

4 - Peel the carrots.

5 - Throw the carrots in the bin. You won't need them. They'll spoil it.

6 - Make sure you've boiled all the eggs.

7 - Fish a dog out of the bins from behind the vets / Martin Clunes' flat.

8 - Warm the plates and lay the table. Did you boil all the fucking eggs?

9 - Shove the eggs up the dogs' arse, serve and eat.

10 - For dessert how about some Vien- etta or a Twix?

here are some of the best things
I found today...

FOOD 'N' THAT

DALSTON 0845 678 9331

	£
CARROT X1	0.34
FAMILY SIZE COCO POPS X48	170.40
540KG BEEF MINCE	1,587.60
INDUSTRIAL PACKET CONDOMS X1	10.00
LITRE BOTTLE BLEACH X200	120.00
KIDNEY BEANS X1	0.78
BIG NATURAL JUGS MAG X1	2.40
CHELSEA BUN X1	0.30
JEDWARD ALBUM X5	39.95
HAMMER X17	84.83
FILO PASTRY 40M X2	28.50
ANUSOL 25G	3.50

TOTAL	
MAESTRO UK SALE	2,048.60
AID	2,048.60
NUMBER : A000050234	
PAN SEQ NO: ¤¤¤¤¤¤¤¤¤¤¤¤2263	ICC
AUTH CODE : 09	
MERCHANT : 01254	
START : 46200802	
CARDHOLDER PIN VERIFIED : 03/10 EXPIRY 02/14	

CHANGE DUE

0.00

================================

CARDCLUB STATEMENT

================================

MR J PAXMAN
CLUBCARD NUMBER 64565709¤¤¤¤
POINTS THIS VISIT
CLUBCARD POINTS

1,567
1,000,345

================================

12/06/13 13:25 075 0768 3221

SEXY CHRIS

Well, he's an owl which means that from a distance he looks like any other owl to be honest. To be even more precise he's a Tawny Owl which mean's he's stocky, medium-sized and he's a sort of filthy brown/grey colour.

Take a few steps closer and you'll notice that he's wearing cowboy boots and has a tattoo of Kurt Cobain on his left wing. (He basically looks like a right cunt.) He's quite threadbare for an owl because his feathers haven't grown back properly after the time that I dared him to pluck them all out and he almost died.

He also has a beak in the middle of his face. He's heard people saying that owls are intelligent and he believes his own hype. At the moment he's trying to read The God Delusion by Richard Dawkins but he keeps dropping it out of his tree and his reading glasses keep falling into the canal because he doesn't have any fucking ears. It doesn't matter anyway because we all know he can't read for toffee.

He can be alright though. Sometimes he makes me laugh. A few weeks ago he dropped a grass snake onto Princess Anne's head from about 50 ft, just for a laugh.

sexy Chris CROSSWORD

3 JULIANROUNDHOUSE
5 BETHANYLOUGNE
6 BIGMINGE
LUKEPRINGLES
8 REBECCAFLUTE
9 BRENDAHOOVER
10 SIMONRICHARDS
14
15
16 JASONHOLIDAY
1 THOMASCUNTER
2 KARLKRANCH
11 HOLLYPOOK
12 CHEEKYJACK
13 NICKFLITWICK

Across

3. Ate his own legs in a car park last year
5 LEZZA! (owl)
6 The answer is **BIG MINGE**
7 Trout
8 Died last week. Vole
9 Badger. Her name's Brenda Hoover
10 A dog i know with aids
14 I saw him kick a dog to death behind PC World **this morning**
15 Arrogant chaffinch
16 Pigeon. No feet. **Cunt**

Down

1. Fox. Claimed his grandad invented mountain bikes. Bullshitter
2 A duck who looks a bit like Kris Akabusi
4 Is he a rook or a crow? Perhaps even a raven? I don't know. Never been able to tell the difference to be completely honest with you. He has an enormous penis anyway
11 Fox. Went on to become a posh hat
12 He's a horse. I once climbed up his arse when it was snowing.
13 He's some kind of vole. He's usually dressed in motorcycle leathers

ANT-DOKU

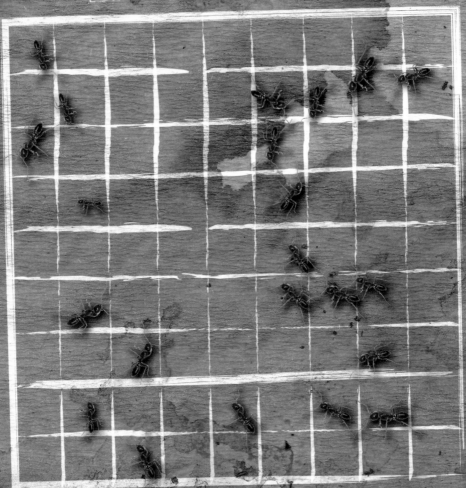

JUST FILL THE SQUARES UP WITH ANTS!!! IT'S THAT SIMPLE.

THINGS THAT I'VE FORCE FED TO SWANS

```
Z C W G Y A K U L 5
E O G L P I N S N M
O G H H A W Z P Q I
X S S F U I J K A C
A R E D L E A T H E R   S O F A
N B X H F K L Q O T
T B Y V L W P Z O S
S U C G O D E J V O
A X H E O D N K E I
A T R S D L F M R L
    I
    S
```

BIN POKER

INSTRUCTIONS FOR A SORT OF CARD GAME
SEXY CHRIS AND MYSELF MADE UP.
...SOMETHING TO KILL A BIT OF TIME IF
YOU'RE AT A LOOSE END AND YOU'RE BORED
OF BUGGERING SWANS.

WHAT YOU NEED

A pack of cards
(Don't need the 8 of
diamonds)
Dice (several)
12 dozen eggs
A child's shoe
Twigs/soil
Bog roll

Deal the cards; 8 for the dealer, 10 for
Sexy Chris.
Roll the dice. It's a 4. That means you
take one of the twigs/handful of soil.
Roll again.
ROLL AGAIN!
If it's an even number then smash an egg.
If it's an odd number then move back to the
start.
Deal the cards again and again until
someone gets an ace.
7, 5, Jack, 2...And so on.
Sexy Chris has the ace. Now he has to put
an egg into the child's shoe and luzz it
into the canal.
Remember that if someone rolls a 6 after
they've laid down a queen then the game is
over. No one wins.
9 of clubs? Very nice.
Roll again and again and again until
someone is victorious.
The person with the least amount of soil
at the end is the overall winner.
Force-feed any remaining eggs down Sexy
Chris' throat. Point and laugh whilst Sexy
Chris cries and vomits at the same time. I
fucking hate Sexy Chris.

GOT MY HEAD STUCK IN A HOLE. A FIREMAN'S PUTTING THINGS (TOY CARS, COINS ETC) UP MY ARSE WHICH ISN'T MUCH FUCKING HELP

An IDEA for a NEW PERFUME

Name : Don't know, something like 'Vixen' or 'Cistern' or something like like that.

Tag line : Mmmmm. That smells nice.

Ingredients(?) : Fog, turmeric, tears, champagne and bees(98%)

What does it smell like? : Not great. I'm not going to lie to you it doesn't smell great at all.

Who's advertising it on the bloody poster? : Well it's a fragrance for a man or a woman so maybe someone like Angelina Jolie for the girls and someone like Nick   Faldo for the boys.

The TV ad : Maybe something like...It's set in a big warehouse full of tinned tuna. There's a man unbuttoning his shirt (maybe he works here in the warehouse? Maybe he's a fisherman - It's not clear). Anyway he's striding through this massive fuck off warehouse like he owns the place and he's fit as arseholes. (Everything's in black and white and we've got Sigur Ros pounding away in the background.) The man walks up to a woman who's leaning against a digger and they start getting off with each other. After a couple of seconds the man explodes and turns into a swarm of bees. The woman screams and starts to have a panic attack. The camera zooms into the woman's eye and we see the bottle of this perfume. The voice over (Professor Brian Cox?) says "Mmmmm. That smells nice" and then it's basically just a case of sitting back and waiting for the bunce to come rolling in.

HOW to have
SEXUAL INTERCOURSE

First and foremost it's important to find someone who is/isn't up for it (sex). This could be just about anyone; your wife/boyfriend/slut/dog/ neighbour's dog.

Approach your target (try not to refer to them as a 'target'). Strike up conversation but be sure to keep it erotic. Tell her/him/it that he/she/it looks 'fuckable' (use the word 'fuckable' as often as possible). Make some more crude remarks. Smile. If it feels appropriate then do that little hand gesture where you make a circle with two fingers and then poke at it with an extended digit.

Once you're certain that this person doesn't work for the Metropolitan Police then it's time to drag them back to your luxury hotel room/caravan /disgusting corner.
Set the mood. Mince around the place lighting candles and laughing. Remember this is supposed to be fun.

Ask your lover if they'd like to put some music on. If they didn't bring any music then shout at them. Force them to sing. Make them dance. Create an uncomfortable atmosphere before apologising profusely for your dreadful behaviour.

CHAMPAGNE! (apologise for not having any Champagne)

Ask/force your lover to wash. (If you're also covered in soil then it might be a good idea to join them in the shower). This can be a great opportunity to try out a bit of 'foreplay'. Kiss his/her neck. Fondle their ears. Stick your fingers up his/her bum.

Return to the bedroom. If your partner seems frightened/disorientated then help them to remove all of their clothes. They'll be all wet now after that shower. Perhaps your partner is in the early stages of hypothermia. That would explain the far away look in their eyes. Keep talking to them. Say things like "I can't wait to see your penis" or "I'm still well up for a bit of slap 'n' tickle if you are". Stroke their hair.

Climb into the bed/nest/bin and let the sex commence. Go absolutely mental. Do whatever comes into your head. Shout, scream, applaud, laugh, spit and fire jets of milk out of your nose. Act like you've been possessed by some kind of bonkers sex demon.

Have a little sleep.
Repeat this process as many times as you like until your knob or fanny hurts /the authorities arrive.

Apologise to your lover for a) Making them cry, and b) Giving them aids.

Kick them out into the cold.

Enjoy the rest of the afternoon and give yourself a big pat on the back.

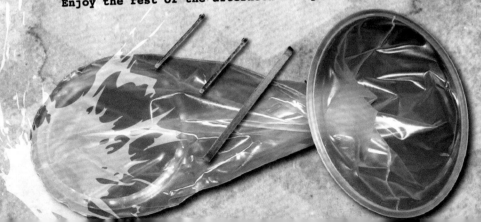

best thing i've ever found a bin

A BIG FUCK OFF DILDO COVERED IN WASPS

KEITH RICE

I've only known Keith Rice for a few days but he seems alright. He's a badger so obviously he looks ridiculous. Keith is quite a grumpy character. He's pretty much constantly fucked off about the fact that the government have decided to murder him and all his mates over the coming years. Facially he looks pretty much exactly like Gary Lineker.

He also carries a gun in a holster.

TOP TEN TYPES of SOIL
with Keith Rice

1. Damp soil.
2. Sort of brown soil, not too brown, mainly black but sort of brown soil.
3. Brown soil.
4. Very hard soil. Compacted and dry.
5. Dusty soil. The type that gets in your eyes and ruins your day.
6. Terracotta? Does that count? Terracotta?
7. The jet black stuff. (Great for growing veg.)
8. Regular soil.
9. Quite a sandy soil. If you look hard enough you can actually see bits of sand in the bugger.
10. White soil (flight of fancy.)

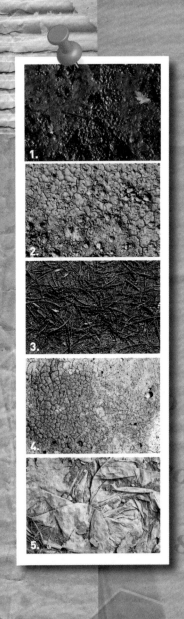

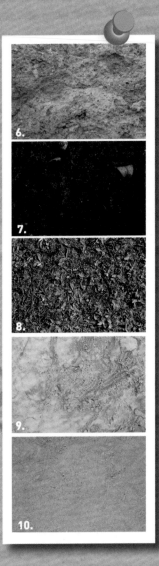

THINGS I'VE SEEN CELEBRITIES DOING

through the blinds/ curtains and that

FELICITY KENDAL

She was in her conservatory (posh). She was wearing a wedding dress and entertaining guests. She was blind drunk and at one point she was sick in a pot plant (some sort of cactus). Eamon Holmes was there. He was playing a trumpet.

VERNON KAY

He was in his shed. It was a nice shed. Quite expensive looking. It almost looked new. Perhaps he'd just built it. That would explain why he was wearing a tool belt and why he was very sweaty. He was wearing a 'Homer Simpson' t-shirt. He was also putting make-up on a horse.

TIM HENMAN

Stood in his living room (pretty much nude). Basically wearing nothing but a pair of l e a t h e r chaps/lederhosen. He was covered in blood and smiling. He kept shout- ing something about apple juice. There were several dogs. His house was engulfed in flames throughout.

ALISTAIR DARLING

This was a few weeks back. He was outside his house in the middle of the night. He had loads of felt pens around him. It looked like he was trying to 'colour his car in'. He was just stood there in a pair of Billabong surf shorts and frantically trying to colour this bloody car in. He kept mumbling things like – "Turn red you cunt" and "why can't you be more red you stupid bastard?"

CORROSIVE

UN 1719

WHAT THE FUCK
IS THIS!?!?!

DOUBLE DENIM DAVID

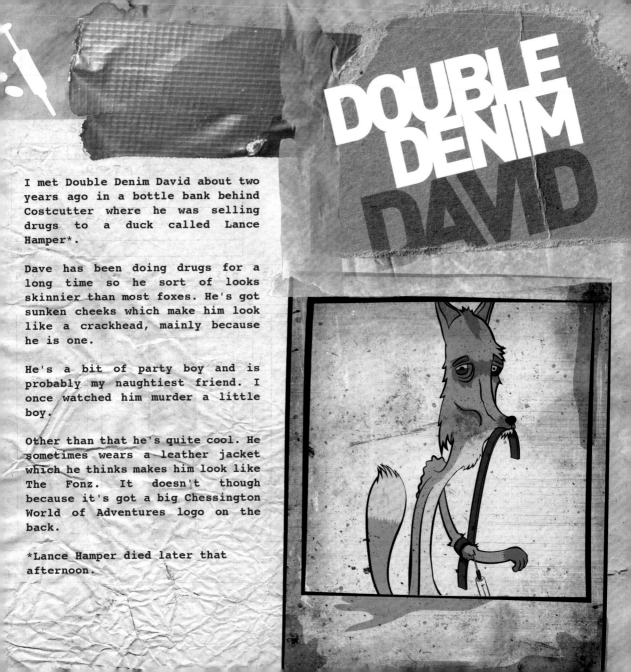

I met Double Denim David about two years ago in a bottle bank behind Costcutter where he was selling drugs to a duck called Lance Hamper*.

Dave has been doing drugs for a long time so he sort of looks skinnier than most foxes. He's got sunken cheeks which make him look like a crackhead, mainly because he is one.

He's a bit of party boy and is probably my naughtiest friend. I once watched him murder a little boy.

Other than that he's quite cool. He sometimes wears a leather jacket which he thinks makes him look like The Fonz. It doesn't though because it's got a big Chessington World of Adventures logo on the back.

*Lance Hamper died later that afternoon.

DOUBLE DENIM DAVID
A Life through the lens

(A retrospective photography exhibition
celebrating the work of Double Denim David)

Portrait of Eddie Young
18x24" digital print
£150

Stick Study
11x14" digital print
£1497

Autumn Crunch
11x14" digital print
£1497

Pipe Dreams
11x14" digital print
£4000

Nucleus
11x14" digital print
£9 999.00

Brave New World
2x4" digital print
£500 000.00

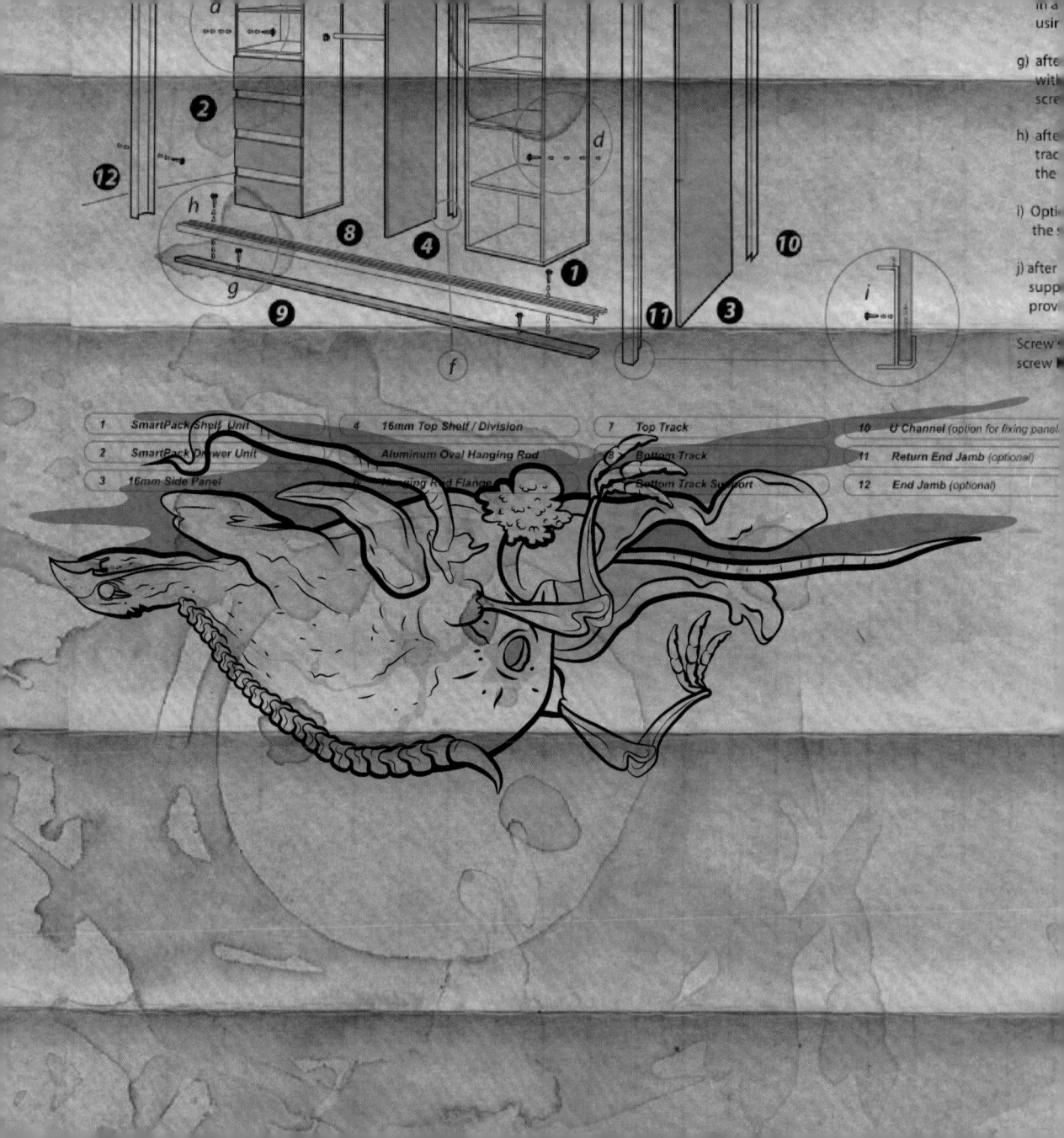

in a
usir

g) afte
with
scre

h) afte
trac
the

i) Opti
the

j) after
supp
prov

Screw
screw

1	SmartPack Shelf Unit	4	16mm Top Shelf / Division	7	Top Track	10	U Channel (option for fixing panel)
2	SmartPack Drawer Unit	5	Aluminum Oval Hanging Rod	8	Bottom Track	11	Return End Jamb (optional)
3	16mm Side Panel	6	Hanging Rod Flange	9	Bottom Track Support	12	End Jamb (optional)

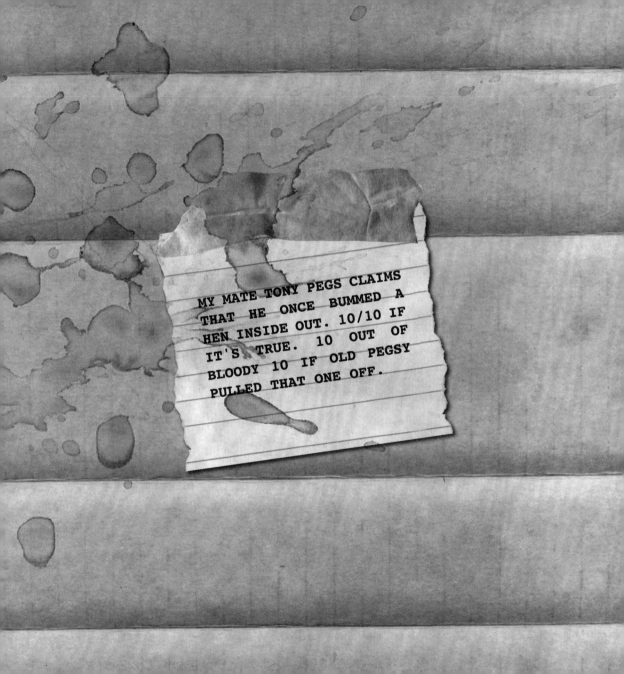

MY MATE TONY PEGS CLAIMS
THAT HE ONCE BUMMED A
HEN INSIDE OUT. 10/10 IF
IT'S TRUE. 10 OUT OF
BLOODY 10 IF OLD PEGSY
PULLED THAT ONE OFF.

GUS

i hAVE STOLEN YOUR bOX
oF WaSPs aND CONdOMS,
if yoU eVER WaN7 tO
seE iT again Meet mE
UndEr THE CaNaL @
MiDNIgHt , i'm
GOing 70 KiCK YOu
iN tHe dIck , i FucKing
hAte YOu

C PACKHAM

THINGS YOU CAN DO TO A FROG

Trap him in an old kettle.

Whisper the word 'clitoris' into his ear on the hour, every hour.

Punch him in the ribs.

Flick raspberries at him from the top of the shed.

Gently shove him down the drains.

Ram him up Keith Bisto's big fat arse.

Super-glue him to Carol Vorderman's mountain bike.

Marry the cunt.

Post him to Malta. (Second class.)

Watch Raiders of the Lost Ark with him and then tear his fucking head off and hurl it into the canal.

Wear him as a sort of posh brooch.

THINGS I'VE PUT IN MY MOUTH in the last 24 hours

1 - My paw.

2 - My tail.

3 - You know those little taps you get on the side of some houses? I think they're probably for a garden hose or something. Little brass taps. Well anyway, I put one of them in my gob and then I put it in my bum.

4 - Lamb (ancient / rank) - I found this in the boot of Gary Barlow's Land Rover. (Under the kites.)

5 - A cygnet*.

6 - Julian Blanch. (a moth.)

7 - Old bread (Hovis, Best of Both - Expiry date 29/10/12).

8 - My left ball/nut - i.e the one that isn't black and revolting and doesn't smell like the end of the world.

9 - Tent pegs / porridge.

10 - Wood lice. (32 of the bastards.)

11 - An AC adaptor for a Panasonic KX T1418 2 Cassette Remote Answering machine.

12 - Clunes / Martin Clunes. (fist/ears/tongue.)

13- Rats.

14 - Wax. (I set my head on fire doing this one - Hahahhahahahaha.)

15- A couple of hours ago I, sort of, licked the exhaust pipe of a van. Does that count? Does that count? I suppose it's my list. Yeah, I licked the exhaust pipe at the back of the van (Citroen Berlingo) and it tasted like soot and I got a bit of an erection and I started crying. It was weird. Won't be making that mistake again.

*Owen Cromwell.

RECIPE #2
DALSTON PAELLA

1 - Find a bin and empty the contents onto some poor fucker's driveway.

2 - Collect the necessary ingredients. (burnt toast, ancient sausages, slugs, shattered eggs, Toilet Duck, faggots, etc).

3 - Carry the ingredients back to your filthy pit/flat and lay them out on the muck/sideboard.

4 - Use your snout/hands to push the ingredients into a sort of pile and then wait for it to become covered in ants. (During this part of the process you may like to spend some time growling at the next door neighbour's motorbike/shrubbery.)

5 - Invite your latest fancy woman/slut over for dinner. It'll be ready soon.

6 - At this point the sun should appear from behind the clouds and heat up the vile concoction. (Spend some time squinting at the sun.)

7 - Tell your friend Sexy Chris that he's not invited. Encourage him to commit suicide. Why's Sexy Chris just sat there staring at you?

8 - Serve on a bin lid and tuck in.

9 - Growl at the wasps throughout the duration of the meal.

10 - Vomit the revolting slop into the canal, make your apologies and carry on about your business. Eat a coot or lick some petrol. Anything to get the horrible taste out of your mouth.

A DESCRIPTION OF SOME OF THE LOCAL BANDS IN THE AREA

BINS
SECTION   MAIN ENTRANCE
ROUND THE BACK BY SHOP'N'THAT

PRESENTS

The COOL LADS

DOORS OPEN 7PM   DATE SOON   PRICE a sock

MEMBERS - 2 coots and a swan (on synths).
FROM - Just sort of up the canal really (near that graffiti of a the chimpanzee with an enormous penis).
INFLUENCES - Kraftwerk, Pet Shop Boys, Prince.
REVIEW - These guys are fucking useless. They've got one shit keyboard between them and they can't even play it properly because they've all got stupid fucking wings. A complete waste of time. Cool Lads? Shit Lads more like!

2/10

LISTEN TO - Donkey On The Dance Floor, Lovely Heron, Love Duck

MEMBERS - A wasp, 3 moths and a horse on drums.
FROM - Catford.
INFLUENCES - Beastie Boys, Shed Seven, Russ Abbott.
REVIEW - These guys are very talented. By mixing early hip-hop with indie guitars and ethereal, ambient soundscapes, these guys have created something truly special. Also the horse is an absolute powerhouse on the drums. Expect to be seeing a lot more of The Sky Eagles. (Shite name.)

10/10

LISTEN TO - Bongo Fury, Dog Goblin, Slippery G

MEMBERS - Just a chaffinch called Don Harris.

FROM - Milton Keynes / An egg.

INFLUENCES - Slayer, Anthrax, Keane.

REVIEW - He's probably the best chaffinch I've ever seen at playing an electric guitar solo. Having said that, I've never even seen another chaffinch even give it a bash and Don basically just perches on the neck and pecks the strings every now and again. He's also a bit of a cunt because he claims that he used to play drums for Megadeth and I know he didn't because he's a fucking chaffinch. Last time I saw him I kneed him in the chest and booted him into the canal.

5/10

LISTEN TO - Knuckle Supper, Fish Frenzy, Pecking Twigs

DON HARRIS

AVERAGE CHAFFINCH

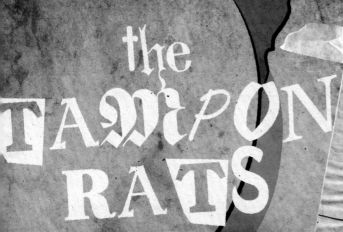

the TAMPON RATS

MEMBERS - A load of rats. FROM — Stoke Newington (Kebabylon). **INFLUENCES -** Bon Jovi, Motley Crue, Kiss. **REVIEW -** Jumping on the 80's hair-metal explosion that seems to be happening in the animal kingdom at the moment, these guys certainly look the business with their long, poodle-permed haircuts and tiny little leather jackets. Problem is, their instruments are just twigs and bits of old rubbish, so they can't actually play any music, and, as such, aren't really a band, instead, they're just a bunch of rats in a bin.

●

0/10

LISTEN TO - N/A

I JUST STOLE A GIRL'S HEART. IT WAS IN THE BINS BEHIND ST THOMAS' HOSPITAL SO I DON'T THINK SHE NEEDS IT ANYMORE.

B INVENTIONS

BIN ROD

Nothing's more frustrating than a dustbin with a lid on it, especially when you know full well that it's absolutely full to the brim with medical waste (bollocks, tits, lungs etc) like the one up at the hospital. The Bin Rod makes lifting the lid off tricky refuse containers an absolute doddle and the carved mahogany handle says "Who's this suave customer?" to any cunt you happen to bump into on your rounds. An absolute must have for the modern gent who enjoys licking vile filth out of bins.

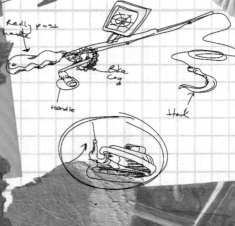

CLIVES GPS TRACKER

Really posh handle

Bike Cog

Handle

Hook

Really posh handle

EEL DUNGAREES (DUNGAREELS?)

Finally, a solution to an age old problem. This one-legged dungaree is just what the doctor ordered for the modern eel with shit to do. Comes with a large front pocket, ideal for carrying rocks, silt, weeds and canned goods up and downstream.

Also available in beige.

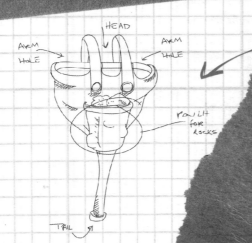

HEAD

ARM HOLE

ARM HOLE

POWLIT FOR ROCKS

TAIL

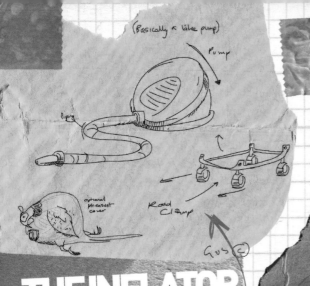

(Basically a lake pump)

Pump

Piping

optional pheasant cover

Road Clamp

Gus ©

MUSICAL SNAKE HELMET

Say goodbye to non-musical snakes with the MUSICAL SNAKE HELMET. The Musical Snake Helmet is a simple transistor radio attached to a small helmet that will fit any grass snake, adder or slow worm. Simply strap the helmet to the nearest serpent and then sit back and let the good times roll.

Requires 12 x 9 volt batteries

THE INFLATOR

It can be dangerous and annoying when you're trying to eat a battered crow that's been squashed in the middle of a dual carriageway and you have to keep running out of the way of traffic to avoid joining the bastard in the afterlife. You can't move it because it's stuck fast with it's guts. Not a problem with THE INFLATOR! The Inflator is a small pump attached to a length of pipe. Simply stick the pipe into the dead cunt's throat and then roll the pump into the path of oncoming traffic. Each time a wheel passes over the pump, a jet of air will be sent into the crow's lungs until eventually it should start to inflate and then you can just roll it off into the woods and eat it in peace. NB: The pump could be disguised as a pheasant so that drivers would aim for it instead of swerving out of its way.

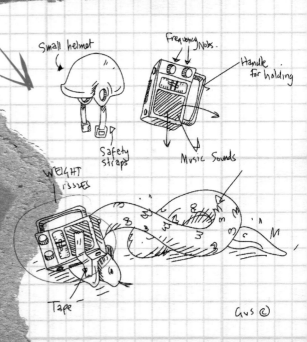

Small helmet

Safety straps

Frequency Nobs.

Handle for holding

Music Sounds

WEIGHT ISSUES

Tape

Gus ©

THE MOUSE CANON / swan pistol

Not sure if anyone will want one of these to be honest. It's basically a sort of gun / crossbow that shoots mice at swans. Don't even know what the point of this is yet to be honest. I've got a good mind to stop building the bugger. I'd quite like it to be mainly digital. Was also thinking it might be quite nice if it had a picture of Pauline Quirk from 'Birds of a Feather' on the handle. I'll be honest, I sort of need to go back to the drawing board on this one a bit. I might fuck this one off actually. Can't exactly see Duncan Bannatyne biting my hand off for this one.

THE NEVER ENDING WASP

Not sure how this would work, but it's basically a wasp that will never grow old and die. It's basically an immortal wasp. It'd be amazing. You'd never be lonely again. Just trying to sort out the nitty-gritty.

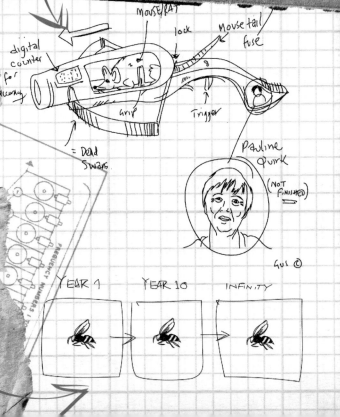

digital counter for accuracy

MOUSE/RAT

lock

Mouse tail/ fuse

Grip

Trigger

= Dead Swans

Pauline Quirk

(NOT FINISHED)

GUS ©

YEAR 1   YEAR 10   INFINITY

I just saw a pig run into an electric fence and soil itself. Magical Stuff.

DREAM DIARY

a description of some recent dreams

MONDAY

It all started in a sort of cave. We were in a cave but it was also raining quite heavily. The whole gang was there (Colin Hong, Keith Rice, James The Haemophiliac Wood Pigeon, etc). The floor of the cave was sort of transparent, as though it was made of glass / crystal. When I looked down I could see all the stars and planets orbiting one another, almost as if we were stood on the edge of the galaxy, looking down over the entire solar system as time moved forwards at millions of light years per second. In the middle of the cave was a tower / church. Everything started to go purple. We went inside the tower and started to climb the stairs which were made of snakes. When we got the top Keith Rice did a shit that looked like Jesus Christ and then I woke up.

TUESDAY

This one started in the sea. I was sat in a boat with Hugh Fearnley-Whittingstall. He kept shooting wood lice at me through a tube of Smarties and I was getting really fed up. We went over a waterfall but it was sort of upside down so we went up into the sky if you can imagine such a thing. When we got up there Hugh had turned into a puffin. He spent the rest of the dream trying to get me on board with his idea to open a factory that produces ball bearings for industrial machinery. I politely declined and his head burst into flames and then I woke up.

WEDNESDAY

Don't remember much about this one. Don't think I had a very good night's sleep owing to the fact that Bruce Forsyth kept crawling into my den and asking to borrow money for the penny nudgers at the amusement arcade. There was something in this dream that I remember actually. There was something about a really poorly horse but I can't remember how it fitted in.

THURSDAY

It started down by the canal behind Kwik Fit. I was trying to find something (food? Could have been food I suppose). Suddenly I noticed all my legs were attached to various ropes and pulleys and I couldn't move. A tramp appeared. It was the one that always hangs around this neck of the woods. The one who dresses like a cowboy and spends the day calling all the ducks a bunch of wankers. The tramp started using me as a puppet and I burst into tears. When I opened my eyes I was in an aeroplane. I was strapped to Gary Lineker's chest and we jumped out. Gary opened his parachute and it ripped his arms off and he started laughing. We fell for what felt like ages until we crashed into the water. I tried to swim to the surface but it was no use as I was being held under by some sort of current. I looked down to see my mate Sexy Chris swimming towards me. He had sort of like a mermaid's tail and a pair of human breasts. He popped one of his tits in my mouth which acted like a scuba diving respirator and I swan to the surface to be greeted by the cast of Dragon's Den who'd all chipped in and bought me a cake.
Then I woke up.

FRIDAY

Had the recurring dream I always have about a donkey with alopecia.

SATURDAY

I looked in the mirror and my head was
made of wasps. Hundreds and hundreds of the
buggers. I yawned and my jaw fell off and grew
a set of tiny little wheels before driving off
into the sunset.
(That was the start of my dream. I'd just eaten quite
a lot of rancid ham that I'd found in the bins behind the
Co-Op so I only have myself to blame to be honest.)
I looked up at the sky and the clouds all sort of coagulated
and turned into Judy Finnigan's head. The head started
smiling at me but then changed it's mind and started crying.
After a few seconds a swan flew out of Judy Finnigan's mouth
and started calling me every name under the sun. I started to
run away. I ran so fast that I travelled back in time. There
was a large explosion. I was sat in a forest dressed like a
Beefeater and all the trees were keys. At the end of the
dream a frog minced up to me, stuck a key in my eye socket
and opened up my head and started filling it with soil.

I woke up in the corner of my pit sweating and vomiting.
Cwis Packham said I had a fever so he took my
temperature by putting a thermometer up my bottom.
It wasn't a thermometer though, it was a Toffee
Crisp. Packham found this about 100 times
more amusing than I did.

SUNDAY

Had a dream that me and Vile Clive built a helicopter out of Alpen.
We kept bickering because Clive said it wouldn't fly unless it was
wearing a wig. It turned out that it didn't fly because it was made
of Alpen. At the end of the dream Vile Clive got raped by a dolphin.

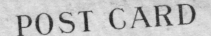

POST CARD

FOR ADDRESS ONLY

PLACE POSTAGE STAMP HERE

FOR CORRESPONDENCE

to GuS tHe FOks

this proovs I hav a washing machine. I hav called it glls The Fox.

I luv you. Can I maRRy you? I hATe you!!
I wont to hAv sex with you.

I like JapANEese pEOple.

iF you don't rite to me this time then I aM GoinG to murder YoO with A Gun.

I dream of yor kisses and wEn I think about Ur sexy GinGer FuR iT makes mY Fanny feel FUNny.

I WaNt To ClimB uP inside Yoll and LiVE iN YouR BuM.

LoVE from Emma Watson

xxxxXXXxxxXXXXxx

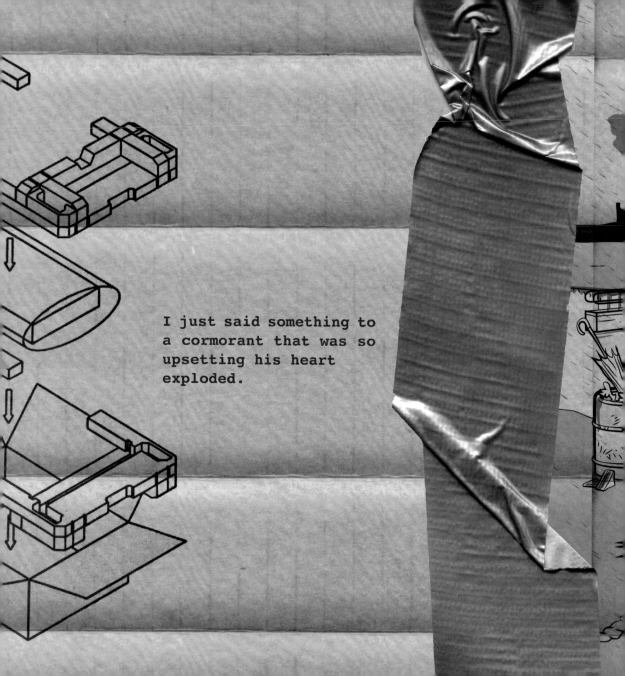

I just said something to
a cormorant that was so
upsetting his heart
exploded.

HEDGEHOGS

A LIST OF REDEEMING FEATURES

Well I'm pretty much coming up with nothing to be honest. They're covered in revolting spines so they aren't worth eating for a kick off. I've basically never met a hedgehog who I didn't think was a complete cunt.

I used to know a hedgehog called Robert Cluster. On one occasion he invited me over to his place for dinner and, as I recall, he spent the entire evening defending the actions of that bozo Ian Huntley. I finished my blancmange, made my excuses and left. You'll certainly do very well to find a bigger tosser than Robert Cluster..

Just spiked a bird bath with gin. Now all the sparrows are fucking and fighting and calling each other cunts.

SOME STUFF ABOUT DRUGS

Believe it or not, drug use is a practice that dates all the way back to prehistoric times. Archaeological evidence suggests that humans have been getting mashed out of their tiny little minds for the last 10,000 years. Basically, your evolutionary process may not have taken quite so long if you lot hadn't spent quite so much time sitting around naked in caves and hallucinating about giant, golden mammoths made of wind.

However, this relationship with narcotics isn't strictly limited to humans. A number of animals consume various psychoactive plants, other animals, berries and even fermented fruit in order to start seeing sounds and hearing colours. It probably won't come as any surprise to anyone to learn that being an animal is an absolute bloody nightmare. Your average urban beast will usually spend the entire day covered in rain, eating dicks and bollocks and narrowly avoiding being bummed and murdered every couple of hours before plodding off back to their filthy, muddy pit to spend the rest of the evening crying and shitting at the same time. The entire thing's about as much fun as eating soil.

Everyone needs a pick-me-up every now and again and the options available to us all are vast. From a glass of red wine in the evening to an intravenous skag hit behind the bins, the drugs menu is a vast spectrum of strengths and flavours with new ones being created every day. And guess what, we've come up with a few that you probably haven't even heard of. Keep your eyes peeled for these cheeky little customers.

DRAKE

ALIAS – Quack, Daffy,

WHAT IS IT? – My mate Double Denim David invented this. It basically consists of licking a duck's eyes. (It works best if the duck is elderly.)

EFFECTS – Gives you an erection. Also makes your head feel like it's full of mice. It's pretty good stuff.

HOXTON HERO

ALIAS – Ian, Bingo Biscuits

WHAT IS IT? – Not sure. Found it in a tub inside Ian Botham's garage in Hoxton. It's white. It looks a bit like emulsion paint. That might actually be what it is to be honest.

EFFECTS – Pretty heavy stuff. Me and my mate Vile Clive did this last week. You snort it. It makes you travel through time. I got so wasted that I started hallucinating. I had a dream that me and Pat Sharp started a long distance lorry driving service. It was off the hook. (When I woke up all my claws had fallen out which is a downside.)

WOOD LICE

ALIAS – Lousse, Cheese, Delicious Chunks

WHAT IS IT? – Wood lice.

EFFECTS – Can't champion this enough. I know drugs are bad but you have to try this. Stick a few wood lice up your arse. It'll change your life. Magical stuff.

STINKY PETER

ALIAS – Pete, The Stench, Funky P

WHAT IS IT? — I found this in a toilet near Kings Cross. It's not very nice. It's like some sort of revolting clay.

EFFECTS — No effects really. Made me a bit giddy I suppose. Just made me feel sick more than anything. I spent the evening vomiting out of my nose whilst weeping and shuddering in the foetal position. Not sure this was a drug actually. Not sure at all.

RIZZLE

ALIAS – The Hump, Kicks, Corden

WHAT IS IT? — This is pretty popular in the fox community. It basically consists of drinking Castrol GTX. You can find it in most garages. It tastes like the end of the world.

EFFECTS — Great stuff. My mate Glen Cake did this a few days ago and got so wasted that he ate his own penis before trying to climb inside his own mind. Not long after that he got the Rizzle Kicks (a sort of convulsive fit) and died. It's a great drug. Great fun. You die about 70% of the time though which is a bit of a nuisance. Last time I did it my eyes went black and Des Lynam ordered me to start a war on PC World. I certainly had a funny five minutes.

DALSTON'S BIGGEST ROBOT BASED PANTO EVER!

PAULINE QUIRKE

IS THE TERMINATOR IN

Terminator 2

the time travelling murderer

DIRECTED BY DANNY DYER'S DENTIST
PRODUCED BY MARTIN CLUNES

CHICO
as
JOHN CONNOR/BUTTONS

CHRISTOPHER BIGGINS
as
T-1000

28th November 2012 - 5th January 2013

BOX OFFICE
0115 989 555

www.royaldalstonplay....co.uk

Found this in
Martin Clunes'
bin this
morning. What
does it mean?

A FEW NEW FILM IDEAS

TIME WOLF (15)

I've had this idea for a film where I play a wolf that can travel through time solving crimes. Think Doctor Who meets Lewis/Morse (meets a wolf). I'd basically fly through time, a complete law unto myself, and duff up criminals like a right proper maverick.

I could have a sidekick played by someone like Kate Humble or perhaps even the gay from Steps.

I wear a bomber jacket for most of the film.
At the end I do this thing where I spark up a cigarette and say something like "Time for dinner" before walking off up the canal.
The main baddie should be played by Clare Balding. That's pretty much a deal breaker.

CLUNES in SPACE (18) (cos of all the wanking)

In this film, Martin Clunes (played by Alan Rickman) is an astronaut who gets lost in space. H
lands on an unknown planet and wanders about trying to find civilisation. After a couple of day
he hasn't found anything apart from a bunch of rocks and he dies.

There's no talking in this film and it's shot in real time.
It's also in black and white.
Quite an arty little customer this one.

THE FROG CHAMP

A gripping thriller in which a frog (called Adam Varnish) gets trapped in a knackered old bath and struggles to climb out. Very CGI heavy.

Soundtrack by Enya.
Ideally I'd like this to be the most expensive film ever made.

DENNIS THE BIN NINJA

Haven't really sorted out the nitty gritty in regards to the plot of this one, but thought it might be nice if there was a scene where someone kicked a dog into the side of a greenhouse and cut its throat open.

18 HARD BOILED MURDER

Sort of cashing in on the whole 'Saw' franchise, a man (Pierce Brosnan) goes around killing people...with eggs. (Not sure how/why. I suppose in one scene he could feed someone fucking loads and loads of the buggers.) The film will be very gritty. There's a bit about racism in it and even a scene where you see a couple of bent fellas going at it hammer and tongs.

SISSONS

A feature length documentary about the life of the news reader Peter Sissons narrated by my mate Keith Rice (a grumpy badger).

Think 'Senna' (but about Peter Sissons instead of Ayrton Senna).

A Chinese lad keeps angling his penis towards me and sort of winking.

A LIST OF 10 ANIMALS AND THE THINGS I'VE SHOVED UP THEIR ARSES

1 - HERON - a Stanley knife, a frog, a Toffee Crisp

2 - BADGER - A small red racing car from a Scalextric

3 - OWL - A horseshoe, a packet of biscuits, a small can of linseed oil, a bag full of bits of wool, some strips of bacon, a travel hairdryer, buttons, a whore's wig, a pipe, 4 or 5 pairs of winklepickers, matches, children's teeth, a padlock

4 - RAT - Coins, cigarettes, a bike pump, a flute

5 - PIG - My mate Les Bunting's head

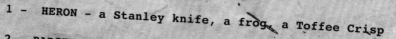

6 - SWAN - A tennis racket, another Stanley knife, another packet of biscuits, another swan, my paw, my head, a crowbar, golf balls, a gold umbrella, a novelty pencil case, wasps, a small dog, a cassette tape of Tubular Bells 2

7 - FROG - Light bulbs, a bomber jacket

8 - DOG - A jar of Sharwood's mango chutney

9 - DONKEY - My mate Ian House, my mate Vile Clive, My mate Sexy Chris, Martin Clunes' acoustic guitar, a TV, petrol, a mountain bike (no wheels), bamboo, a hoover, a torch

10 - I once put a coot up his own arse and it sort of went inside out and everyone started crying because you could see that his heart was still beating.

HOW TO STEAL STUFF FROM JEREMY PAXMAN'S HOUSE

Turn up at 2am on Newsnight. He'll be tuckered out on Newsnight. This is usually the best time to strike.
 Put one foot on the bin and hoist yourself up onto the bus shelter. (Make sure there's no one waiting at the bus shelter or you'll be rumbled before you've even fucking started.)
Keep low.
From here you should be able to peer into Paxman's living room. If he's still in there watching Jurassic Park 3 again then hold fire (listen to some music/play Angry Birds). He'll be done soon.
The lights have gone out.
Hop onto the shed and jump down into the compost heap. Creep up the garden path being careful not to trip over all the toys.
You're at the back door. To your right there should be boot scraper (posh) in the shape of a kangaroo (a gift from Australia? From a friend? Jonathan Dimbleby perhaps). Anyway, under that there are two keys; one for the back door and one for Paxman's full suspension mountain bike.
Break in.
You're in the kitchen. Unplug all the electricals and stack them by the back door. You can collect them on the way out. The cooker will be very heavy so make sure you drag it across the floor very slowly and quietly.
Go through the corridor and into the front room. On the mantelpiece you'll find a large collection of revolting china animals (mainly tigers). Sling them in your sack. You can flog them at the car boot sale on Sunday.

Help yourself to the coffee table, the cushions, the VCR and the picture of Cindy Crawford sprawled over the bonnet of a Ferrari F40.

Pull up all the carpets on the stairs. They look expensive. (QUIETLY! for fuck's sake).

His shoes. Nick his bloody shoes.

Creep upstairs and loot the bathroom. DON'T FORGET THE LIGHT BULBS!

Now into the spare room... Wait! What was that? It looks like you've been rumbled. . .You shouldn't have chiseled off all those bathroom tiles. What the fuck were you thinking? HIDE!

Cower under the spare bed. There are blue lights outside. you've really done it this time.

You're going to get absolutely fucking bollocked if they catch you.

Carry on stealing whatever you find under the spare bed (cassette tapes, Lego etc)

Is that smoke? Did you do that? WHY'S THE FUCKING HOUSE ON FIRE? You've gone too far this time son.

Right there's someone in the room. You're out of time. Are they police? Fucking hell the house is swarming with fucking police.

Grab as much as you can and dive through the window. NOW RUN!

Nevermind your broken ankle. Head back round the corner to the bus stop immediately and wait for a 141.

FILTHY SECRET LONDON SPOTS

Hampstead Heath

Hampstead Heath's great. Due to an oversight by the council, there aren't anywhere near enough bins so it's regularly absolutely covered in crap (I once found an entire packet of sausages.) Many people use the heath for bumming strangers and foxes are no exception. Just last week I popped up there and got off with a swan on Parliament Hill. Word of warning though: On more than one occasion I've wasted time getting into a bin and discovered it's just full of little bags of dog turds. Watch out for this as it can be very annoying.

Cottage Fried Chicken, Dalston

Hackney City Farm

A great place to go if you want to murder a few hens. I'm thrilled that they put farms in the middle of the city so that people like me can, sort of, get back to their roots... (My grandad used to murder hens for a living in Orpington, Kent.) The other day me and my mate Double Denim David took some M-Cat and murdered about 30 or 40 hens and then just hung about until the farmer turned up. When he did he started crying and hurling his packed lunchbox at us. We laughed so much that we were sick. They also have other animals there as well. Once I saw a pig run into an electric fence and soil himself. Magical stuff.

Near where I live, I can quite often be found behind the Dalston Cottage Fried Chicken. I usually just curl up on the air conditioning unit out back and chill out. The whole place stinks of grease and there are bones and bits of chicken all over the place. Martin Clunes and Emma Bunton live in a flat above Cottage Fried Chicken and sometimes we all hang out and they plait my fur and feed me biscuits. I guess, to me, the whole place just feels like home. I've got a lot of happy memories of this place. Once saw a man having a poo in a skip for one. I've got plenty more stories like that as well.

Regents Canal

A few years ago I found a bald rat in the canal and since then it's always held a special place in my heart. The best thing about the canal is probably how much crap people just hurl into it. On a weekend it can look like an absolute pile of shit. Canals in the city attract a lot of colourful characters. The other day I was sucking Bisto out of a tramps trousers under a bridge. Great stuff. One of the problems with Regent's Canal though is the amount of coots who hang about there. In my experience coots are just extremely racist and are always looking for trouble. Last time I was there I punched a coot in the throat for calling me a cunt.

Greenwich Tip

If you're a fan of rats, piles of old shit and other people's rubbish then you won't want to miss out on a trip to Greenwich Tip. It stinks. It absolutely fucking stinks. I was once lucky enough to find a bag full of human hands inside a knackered old fridge. My mate Violent Clive put one on his head and pretended he was a hen. Fantastic. I've never really been to a tip that I didn't enjoy but there's just something about this place. Also if you go in the summer you'll find that the whole place is full of wasps. Doesn't get much better than that.

An OBITUARY FOR A MOTH
ADAM PRICE
2012-2013

Adam Price (a moth) was born in a caravan (in the cupboard bit that contained the boiler) in about June of 2012.

As a youngster Adam would spend his days flying around Bury St Edmunds eating sap, bird droppings, dung, pollen, rotting fruit and generally getting up to all sorts of mischief like any normal boy/moth.

By about October he had developed a passion for flight. He loved to fly. He adored looking down on the towns and cities at night and said that the sensation "gave him the most intoxicating rush". Sometimes he'd fly straight up into the sky, as high as possible, beating his little wings as hard as he could as he went higher and higher. On one occasion he flew so high that he passed out and woke up on top of a lorry in a motorway service station just off the M11.

Adam also had a passion for motorbikes. He'd spend hours sitting in his caravan producing technical drawings and designing tiny little super bikes which he'd send off (first class) to his favourite manufacturers like Yamaha, Kawasaki and Suzuki. Often his designs wouldn't go into production and occasionally he wouldn't even get a reply, but Adam didn't care that much because he was a moth and they don't really have feelings.

On February 15th 2013, whilst flapping around near a shed, Adam was eaten by a Perigrine Falcon and died.

Adam is survived by his sister Beryl Pelvis.

May God have mercy on his soul.

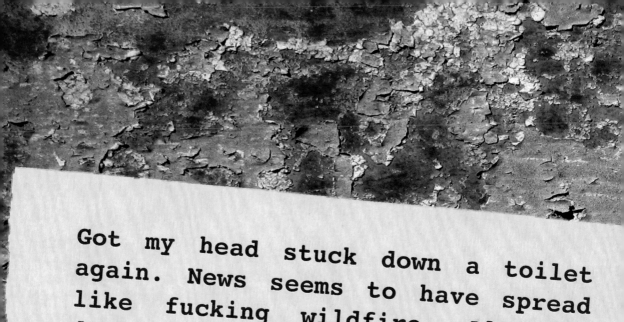

Got my head stuck down a toilet again. News seems to have spread like fucking wildfire. All the ducks are pissing themselves laughing as per usual.

GUIDE to EATING OUT IN LONDON

I'm not much of a cook to be honest. The other day I sucked Bisto out of a prostitute's wig. That was my dinner. You're hardly going to see it on one of Jamie Oliver's menus any time soon (though you might find it on one of Heston's I suppose), which is why I usually go out and leave it to the professionals. Here is my guide to eating out in London. Bon appetit.

THE CANAL

If you enjoy trying different things then pop down to your local canal. Canals are like a street market, thriving with a plethora of different tastes from all over the place. I go to my local one on an almost daily basis. Yesterday I was eating a swan covered in WD40 that I found in a knackered old suitcase and this evening I was slurping beans out of a tramp's Reebok Classic under a bridge. The whole place is like a massive tapas bar full of rubbish and filthy water (like a tapas bar in Magaluf really). Incidentally, if you've never killed, plucked and then eaten a heron you're missing out. Try it now. Delicious.

8/10

Jamie's Italian, Angel

Obviously don't go into the actual restaurant bit because it will cost you an arm and a leg. (An arm and a leg is something you can occasionally find in the canal if you're lucky though — see above.) If you scramble over the bit of corrugated fence next to the bins then you'll find yourself in a bit of disused wasteland containing a fucked-up old Seat Ibiza. If you like good food then this banged out old motor has it all. For starters there are loads of bees in the exhaust pipe. I probably don't need to tell you how tasty bees are when you're sucking them out of a car's tail pipe, Crispy, smokey and a little bit spicy. Very moreish.

For your main course there's a bag of rancid ham on the back seat. It's been there for a few days and it's great stuff. The other day me and my mate Vile Clive had a bit and I don't know what was wrong with it but it made us both go bonkers. Vile Clive ate his own legs and I crawled under a bus and travelled through time. We ended up staying awake for about 80 consecutive hours. I was pretty convinced that my heart was going to explode. Amazing.

And if you're anything at all like me then you'll usually be happy chewing slugs out of your own fur for dessert. All in all a pretty great night out. Bring the missus. Treat her.

9/10

St James' Park at Night

As most of us are aware, David Cameron prowls the area around Whitehall by night and feasts on the flesh and souls of London's wildlife. So not the safest place to be, but if you enjoy a bit of jeopardy with your food then you can do a lot worse than St James' Park at around 4 or 5 am.

Cameron usually hunts in the nude between the hours of 3 and 4 am. He moves around the parks and alleys on his belly (sort of like a python) and catches his prey by firing a web-like substance from his mouth. The whole nasty business is almost as terrifying to behold as it is to become a victim. Which is why I'd advise not arriving too early. Often Cameron will 'over-hunt', so usually if you turn up shortly after his killing spree there is a pretty decent spread on offer, and one which any true Londoner should encounter.

If you're lucky you'll be treated to one of the pelicans which are left in the park as an avian sacrifice. The bird will be coated in Cameron's web-goo which compliments the tender flesh of the bird like a makeshift batter. Salty and quite bitter, it certainly is an acquired taste, but one certainly worth experiencing for the adventurous diner.

7/10

Noel Fielding's bin

Noel Fielding lives in flat with a family of swans in a rough part of Kentish Town. This is pretty much common knowledge. What isn't common knowledge is the culinary jamboree usually on offer inside Noel Fielding's wheelie bin. Hammered rats, scorched dogs, ducks turned inside out and moth kebabs are just a few of the fucked up dishes often on offer in Fielding's bin.

When it comes to butchering animals Fielding is an artist and a visionary (and perhaps slightly bordering on the psychopathic). If I had a pound for every time he's tried to feed me broken glass or shoot me with his harpoon gun I'd be a very rich fox. The fact is, Fielding gets a great deal of pleasure out of killing, torturing and mutilating the wildlife in London. Why? I don't know. All I know is that his 'objects d'art' are a taste sensation. Have you ever eaten a terrapin that's been force-fed a roman candle? No? Well you must because it really is the stuff of dreams. Get down there as soon as possible and enjoy this unique taste sensation before Fielding gets banged up in prison again.

10/10

Stringfellows, Leicester Square, Soho

Ever licked jizz off bathroom tiles? You should. It's not bad. Not bad at all.

6/10

I'm trapped in a bin whimpering. Every time someone comes and tries to help me I bite their hand because I'm a dick.

agony fox
the world's worst agony uncle.

Dear Gus, I have a family of slowworms under my shed, how do I get rid of them, the wife's terrified of the blighters?

Laurence

I once met a slowworm who shared his name with Paul Gascoigne. His name was Paul Gascoigne. Hope this helps.

Heading to the cinema at the weekend — what should I go watch?

Tom

The last film I saw was over at Martin Clunes' flat. I don't know if it's going to be at the cinema any time soon because he made it himself, but it's one of the best films I've ever seen. The first 45 minutes is just a load of close-up footage of Clunes flicking slugs into his desk fan and then it sort of evolves into a kind of drama whereby Clunes runs around his garden dressed as a Canadian Mountie pretending to solve crimes.

It's all filmed in real time on his JVC Compact Cassette Camcorder and pretty much abides by the avant-garde techniques outlined in the 'Dogme '95 film-making manifesto'. It's fucking off the hook. My favourite scene is the part where someone hurls a dog into the side of a greenhouse.

Keep your eyes peeled for this little gem because it's an absolute Tour de Force.

Hi Gus

All the kids on my street seem to be listening to this dubstep stuff. What's your take on it, think it'll stick around or is it just a fad?

Cheers

Dodge, Bristol.

Hi Dodge,

I think it's safe to say that most musical styles are faddish and if you immerse yourself too much, then it's not going to be long before you end up looking like the world's biggest cunt. At the moment, 1980's hair-metal is making a pretty big comeback around the bins. Everyone's back-combing their fur/feathers and listening to Anthrax and Megadeth. As per usual my mate Sexy Chris has taken it too far. Have you ever seen an owl on a tiny little Harley Davidson? He looks like fucking idiot.

Dear Gus, my roommate is doing ab crunches and sit ups and it's really getting intense, he's using the exit door to jam his feet under, what should I do?

Jake

Bodybuilding can be very addictive and, these days, people love working out until they look like a swollen pile of pepperami sausages with a stupid little head poking out of the top like a tortoise trying to climb out of a bin full of knackered old tits behind a hospital.

I used to know a swan called Gareth Bench who went down a similar route. He worked out morning, noon and night, opening and closing the lock gates down by the canal until his muscles were so big that he couldn't even fly or swim anymore. His once slender neck started to look like a doner kebab and all his feathers fell out because he'd only been eating Weight Gain 5000 instead of fish. In the end he ended up getting clubbed to death by some terrified looking men from the local council.

Hope this helps.

agony fox
the world's worst agony uncle

Gus,

My boss (who's a bit gross) keeps staring at me in a strange, leery way. I keep talking about my "husband" really loudly (I don't have a husband) but he won't stop. I'm finding it tough not to get angry with him but I don't want to lose another job. Have you ever had a similar experience?

Amy

Not really Amy. Sometimes Cwis Packham looks at me like he wants to bum me but then I just tell him that I saw a Pied-billed Grebe or a Broad-billed Sandpiper and he'll usually get distracted. If he's really into birds then perhaps you could try this method as well. And if talking loudly about your pretend husband doesn't work then perhaps you could try talking about the terrible condition you keep your underpants in. Refer to them as 'skid city' and tell him that you're going to have to burn them when you get home because you don't think the washing machine is up to the job. That'll probably see him off.

Hi Gus,

The Battery on my Alfa Romeo is constantly flat. I have to jump start it every morning. It's a 159 diesel. Five years old. Any pointers?

Tom C

Don't really know what you're on about mate. My mate Sexy Chris (owl) ate a battery once for a bet. At first it didn't do anything, but later on, whilst he was evacuating it from his bowels, it gave him a little electric shock on his bottom and he fell off a lamp post and landed on a Vauxhall Frontera and shit himself. I laughed so much that burst a I blood vessel in both of my eyes. It was fucking funny.

Hope this is useful.

Gus,

You have a strong Twitter following. I have 16 followers. Sixteen. Why?

Bill Mohin

Hi Bill

I would imagine it's because you're a bit of a knob. I'm just sort of throwing stuff out there really but I imagine you're the kind of guy who turns up at the party dressed as an owl and ruins it for everyone else by spending the whole night eating mice and then coughing them back up in the form of little pellets full of bones. You probably spend the whole night spinning your head round and talking bollocks about Sartre and Nietzsche just because everyone thinks owls are intelligent. But they're not. They're just big feathery benders. Hope this helps. Sorry if you happen not to be an owl.

Gus,

How do I explain to my colleague at work that I just don't want to hear about her boring stories all the time? She goes on about the dullest things but I don't want to be rude.

Help!

Jo

This old chestnut. I had a similar problem with my mate Malcolm Plough. He talks at length about stuff that's so boring that I quite often start to black out and hallucinate. The other day we got trapped in a shed together and he spent about nine hours talking to me about the advantages of having Venetian blinds over standard width pencil pleat curtains, which is probably one of the most pointless discussions a couple of foxes could have when they're trapped in Sir Trevor McDonald's tool shed. By the end I'd had enough and I ended up punching Malcolm so hard that all his hair fell out and he passed away. I feel bad about that now.

Hope this of some use.

Gus, old pal. What's the difference between APR and fixed rate mortgages? I'm in a world of pain here.

Will Keggin

I think they might be two different species of moth. I'm not really sure I can help you on this one mate. That would be my guess though. Gus

Every time I try to cook coq au vin the red wine turns the chicken purple. What can be done?

Rose

This reminds me of the time my mate Quiet Paul put his cock in the exhaust pipe of a van for a laugh. Unfortunately for Quiet Paul it got snagged on a bit of rusty metal and he couldn't get it out. When the driver turned on the engine it backfired and blew his cock off and sent it flying into a bottle bank. We all laughed so much that we started crying blood. It was one of the best days of my life. Paul died a couple of days later from his injuries. What a character. Never a dull moment with that guy. Hope this helps.

My daughter wants a pet. What should I consider and what should I steer clear of?

Paulo

I don't know what it is with you humans and 'owning' animals. I don't know why you feel like you have to possess things and keep them under lock and key just to enjoy them. It's proper fucked up. A few months ago I was walking up the canal, minding my own business, when I was rugby tackled to the ground by news reader Moira Stuart. She fed me a bunch of pills, hogtied me and chucked me into the back of her van. When I woke up a few hours later, I was in a cage in her bungalow. I remember her staring at me with her mad grin and saying "You're my new pet. I'm going to call you Harold Bishop". She'd obviously completely lost the fucking plot. I was trapped there for several days eating Pop-Tarts that she fed me through the bars of my cage whilst she sat in a grubby armchair in her dressing gown watching Reservoir Dogs again and again on her VHS player. One morning after Moira Stuart accidentally fired the scolding, molten contents of a choco-mallow Pop-Tart into her own eyes, I made good my escape, and I never went back. In answer to your question then, consider something like a dog and steer clear of things like eels and woodlice.

Gus,

I live in a beautiful area of the countryside and I was a little troubled to read that people have been rounding up urban foxes into big vans, driving them out of the city, and dumping them in the countryside. I recently spent a fortune on a conservatory, and really can't afford to have my house price devalued because of an influx of the likes of you. Is there any truth behind these rumours of fox dumping, and if so, what should I be doing to stop it?

Best wishes

Paul, Henley-on-Thames

Alright you prick.

Yeah it's true. A few months ago I got my head stuck down a toilet in Dixon's and got slung into the back of a van and driven to Tunbridge Wells in Kent. It was bloody awful. I got chased across a field by some cock in a little red jacket who kept blowing a little trumpet. Eventually he rugby tackled me to the ground and bummed me up against a tree. It was shit. We don't want to be sent to the cunt-ryside any more than you want us to be sent there, mate. It's a crap idea thought up by morons who don't understand anything about the city or the countryside. Having said that, I'll be sure to curl one out on your conservatory if I ever get the chance you fat dickhead.

Falling for a girl at work. Pretty sure she likes me too. We work quite closely together. Is it madness to start something up with someone I see for so much of the working day?

Luke

I keep accidentally getting married to moths. I'm married to about eleven or twelve moths now. I don't know what the fuck's wrong with me but I'm probably not the best person to talk to about matters of the heart. I don't think being close for long periods of time should be a problem though. I once knew a pair of conjoined frogs called Harry and Sam Robinson and they got on famously. They were joined at the hip and they looked like something from the ninth circle of hell, but they were nice lads. A proper good laugh. I killed them, fucked them and ate them for a bet. I regret that now.

Hope this is of some use.

LONELY HEARTS

MISERABLE SWAN (20-25) seeks glum duck for gloomy walks up the canal and depressing relationship.

THOMAS FLASK (Kestrel) looking to meet other falcons for deviant liaisons involving stupidly large dildos (NO OWLS)

TROUT. Ideally looking for a partner called Bethany Keek if at all possible (any age).

SUCK MY COCK! Bastard (Fox) seeks slag/slapper for abusive relationship resulting in a violent (bloody) murder.

LONELY HUMAN (male, creepy little eyes) seeks thick badger for midnight walks, snacks and a generally confusing relationship that will probably end in a lengthy jail sentence. Contact Cwis.

I'M AN EEL CALLED FRANK FLEECE. I'm 34 and I look like a knackered old hose pipe. I'm looking to meet someone who enjoys swimming up and down the river sucking up silt and getting swept down weirs. I also have aids.

WASP seeks bee for pointless afternoons spent trapped in the shed, banging into the window.

ECCENTRIC OTTER (76) looking for a relationship with an animal, human or other. Last wife was an old shoe and it didn't work out. (NO SHOES).

RAPE VICTIM (Fox). Raped a few weeks ago by a horny milkman in the middle of the night. Looking for tentative relationship that doesn't really go anywhere. Lots of tears guaranteed. Call Gus.

RAT (OLD / BENT) looking for that special someone. Must be fond of wandering through piles of old shit and eating all sorts of fucking crap out of bins.

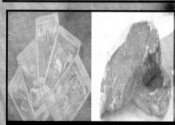

🔍 CLASSIFIED

FOR SALE

2 WASPS
One called Ryan House the other yet to be named - Found in a spiders web - Both dead.
Call DDD - 003

1 X OLD BOOT
Left foot, size 13, laces included, minor damage and possibly haunted - $4.50.
Call Gus - 732

OWL PELLETS
Various sizes and ages - A general mass of undigested bits of food (plant matter, bones, fur, feathers, bills, claws, teeth etc) that I've regurgitated in the form of a filthy pellet. - Starting at $300/lb
Sexy Chris - 909

A PROSTITUTE'S WIG
Brown, stinks, covered in bits of Alpen. Once owned by TV's Cwis Packham. Buy before 30th November and receive a free bag of dog dirt.
Call Vile Clive - 021

WANTED

PHOTOGRAPH OF GARY LINEKER SAT ON A PARK BENCH, TUCKING INTO A TWIX / TOFFEE CRISP.
Also interested in photographs of dogs with their heads stuck in bottle banks - Will pay up to £25 000
Call Clunes - 667

LOST

KNACKERED OLD KETTLE FULL OF BEES
White, plastic and covered in muck. Full to the brim with bees. Great sentimental value.
If found please return to Jeremy Paxman - 856

HOROSCOPES

ARIES
A spot of romance puts a spring in your step. This week you'll fall in love with a swan called Paul Fist, but things may take a nasty turn when he gets run over by a Vauxhall Frontera on the dual carriageway.

TAURUS
YOU'RE GOING TO SHATTER YOUR FUCKING KNEECAPS MATE!

GEMINI
Tread carefully and be wary of what you eat this week. Martin Clunes has got it in for you and I wouldn't be surprised if he poisons your dinner or something. He's done it before. Apparently he did it to Robert Horn and his head went all weird and he coughed up his lungs.

CANCER
This week you need to think for yourself. Just because all the other owls are getting their ears pierced doesn't mean you should as well. You'll end up looking like a right fucking cock end.

PISCES
Your mate Sexy Chris is going to show you his penis. You didn't even ask to see it. What the fuck is Sexy Chris playing at now?

LEO

You're going to have an absolute shocker this week. All the rats and squirrels are going to give you a hard time not to mention the fact that you're going have to put up with the ducks laughing at you as per usual. I'd probably just stay at home if I was you. Chill out.

VIRGO

You're strongly advised to stay up all night, growling at Carol Vorderman's mountain bike.

LIBRA

You're going to get bummed by a gang of bin men.

SCORPIO

Murder Colin Hong.

SAGITTARIUS

Have you got a nosebleed? I think you've got a nosebleed. You probably got it laughing at that donkey with the weird shaped head.

CAPRICORN

You're going to get confused and punch a prostitute in the throat. Try and focus. Don't let this minor hiccup distract you too much. You still need to get a job or Brenda's going to leave you.

AQUARIUS

This week's mainly going to be about hens wearing brogues. That's going to be mainly what you have to deal with this week I'm afraid.

Last Will and Testament

of

GUS

(Full Legal Names)

GUS THE FOX

Specific Gifts and Legacies

I Give

Wasp collection - Offer to Colin Hong. If he doesn't want them then lob them into the canal.

Heart, Lungs, Fur, Claws, Guts, etc - Leave outside Jeremy Paxman's camper van in a bucket as per his request.

Brain - Place in envelope and post to a hospital (abroad).

Kettle full of cocks - Auction at Christie's and give profits to Sexy Chris. If it doesn't sell then point and laugh at Sexy Chris. Make him feel absolutely dreadful. Encourage him to take his own life.
(Hand him a gun / mallet).

Donald Trumpet - Return to parents. (I think they live in Epping now.)

Bags of soil – Send to my cousins (Timothy and Invisible Richard – NOT Greg. Greg gets nothing.)

The mice – Destroy them all. (Except Nigel Philips. Let him live. Send him back to his filthy nest. Let him tell the rest of those bastards what happens when you fuck with old Gus.)

Um Bongo cartons – Bag up, label, place in chronological order and archive in museum.

Testicles – If they're still attached – which I fucking doubt – then slice the buggers off and hurl them through Martin Clunes' velux window.

Bomber Jacket – Return to Keith Rice. Tell him I never wore it. Tell him it's shite and that you'd have to be a right cunt to even be seen dead in it.
(N.B – Don't let me be seen dead in it.)

M-Cat / Gin – Give to Double Denim David if he hasn't popped his clogs first.

Swords and guns– Leave in playground. (St Matthew's Primary.)

House – Burn to the ground. (Before Cwis Packham can get in there and inspect my stools live on the Beeb.)

I JUST SAW A CAT
GET HIT BY A VAN.
I SAT WITH HIM
WHILE HE DIED.
QUIETLY WHISPERING
THE WORD CUNT INTO
HIS EAR AS HE
SLIPPED AWAY.

First published in 2013 by
Short Books
3A Exmouth House
Pine Street
EC1R 0JH

10 9 8 7 6 5 4 3 2 1

A CIP catalogue record for this book is available from the British Library.

ISBN 978-1-78072-177-4

Printed and bound in Great Britain by Butler, Tanner & Dennis
Cover design: Nick Reyniers

Gus would like to Blame: Robert Kirby, Rebecca and Short Books, Tom and Shortlist Magazine, Sonya and Timeout Magazine, Doc Brown, Noel Fielding, Cwis Packham, James the Haemophiliac Wood Pigeon, Lauren Laverne, Leanne, Eddie, Jill, Neha, all the Twitter followers and Clunes.